Brachiosaurus
The nosy dinosaur

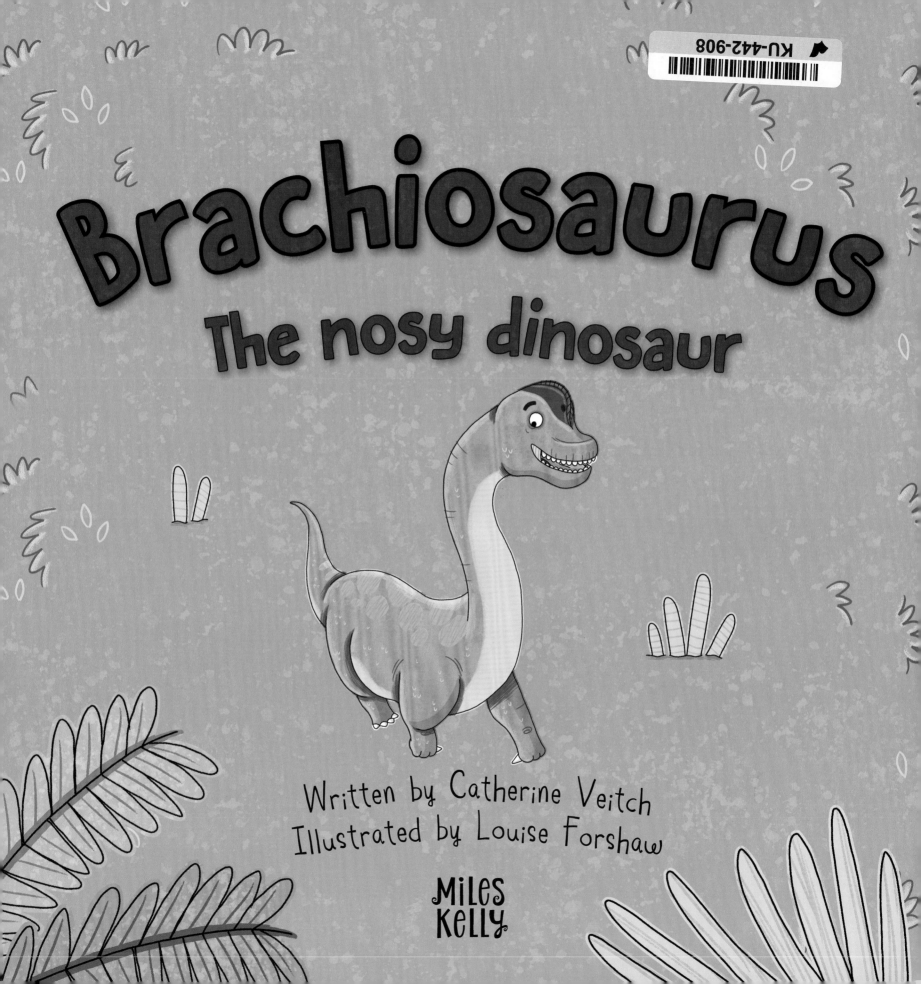

Written by Catherine Veitch
Illustrated by Louise Forshaw

MiLES
KELLY

Millions of years ago, huge dinosaurs with very long necks feasted on forest leaves.

Bobby the Brachiosaurus wasn't fully grown yet, but he still had a very, very long neck.

Bobby's favourite thing to do was use that long neck to be as nosy as possible!

One day, Bobby was munching on leaves as usual when Posy the Podokesaurus rushed by, carrying some moss in her mouth.

"What are you doing, Posy?" Bobby asked.

But Posy had disappeared behind a bush.

And because Bobby was nosy, he stretched his looooong neck over the bush to see where Posy had gone.

WAAAH! WAAAH!

"Bobby! You've woken my babies!" cried Posy.

Bobby stretched his very long neck to **peep behind** the rock. He gently nudged a snoring dinosaur.

"What are you doing?" grumbled a grumpy Brachytrachelopan called Ben. "I was fast asleep before you stuck your nose in! **Go away!**"

Bobby's day was **not** going well.

He was feeling a bit **sorry for himself** when he saw a group of Yandusaurus playing tag.

'That looks fun!' thought Bobby, so he **set off** after them.

The Yandusaurus zipped through the forest. They were much **smaller** and **speedier** than Bobby.

They **leapt** over logs, **skidded** round trees and **squeezed** under branches, until...

...Bobby lost them. He stretched out his long neck to **look around.**

He was about to give up and go home when he heard some **giggling** from behind a clump of trees.

As Bobby's head and neck squeezed through, he saw the Yandusaurus throwing leaves over each other.

Bobby laughed and one of them spotted him.

ROARRRRR!

"Hey, what are you doing, nosy?" cried Yasmina, the eldest Yandusaurus.

Then in the distance there came a loud "ROARRRRRRRRR!" "Megalosaurus! RUN!" shouted Yasmina.

But Bobby's head and neck were stuck fast between the tree branches!

"HELP!" cried Bobby. "My head's stuck!"

The Yandusaurus sped back to help.

They climbed on top of each other until they'd made a **tall tower.** Then the littlest Yandusaurus at the top pushed Bobby's head, hard.

But the Yandusaurus weren't **strong enough** to push Bobby out.

Old Ben heard all the noise and came to **help**. "Let's try pulling Bobby out," he said.

So the Yandusaurus and Ben
all grabbed hold of Bobby's tail.
"One...two...three...PUUULLL!"

All the dinosaurs **pulled** as hard as they could. But Bobby was still stuck fast.

"Again!" yelled Ben. And he pulled so hard he toppled **backwards**.

Luckily, the little Yandusaurus managed to **scramble** out of the way before being **squashed**.

Suddenly, Posy arrived with her babies.

"Help!" called Bobby. "I'm Scared!"

Then Pablo, one of the Podokesaurus babies, had an **idea**. He grabbed a **big leaf** and scrambled along Bobby's back.

Carefully, Pablo crawled through the branches onto Bobby's head.

"Be careful Pablo," cried Posy. The roars were **getting louder** as the Megalosaurus got closer.

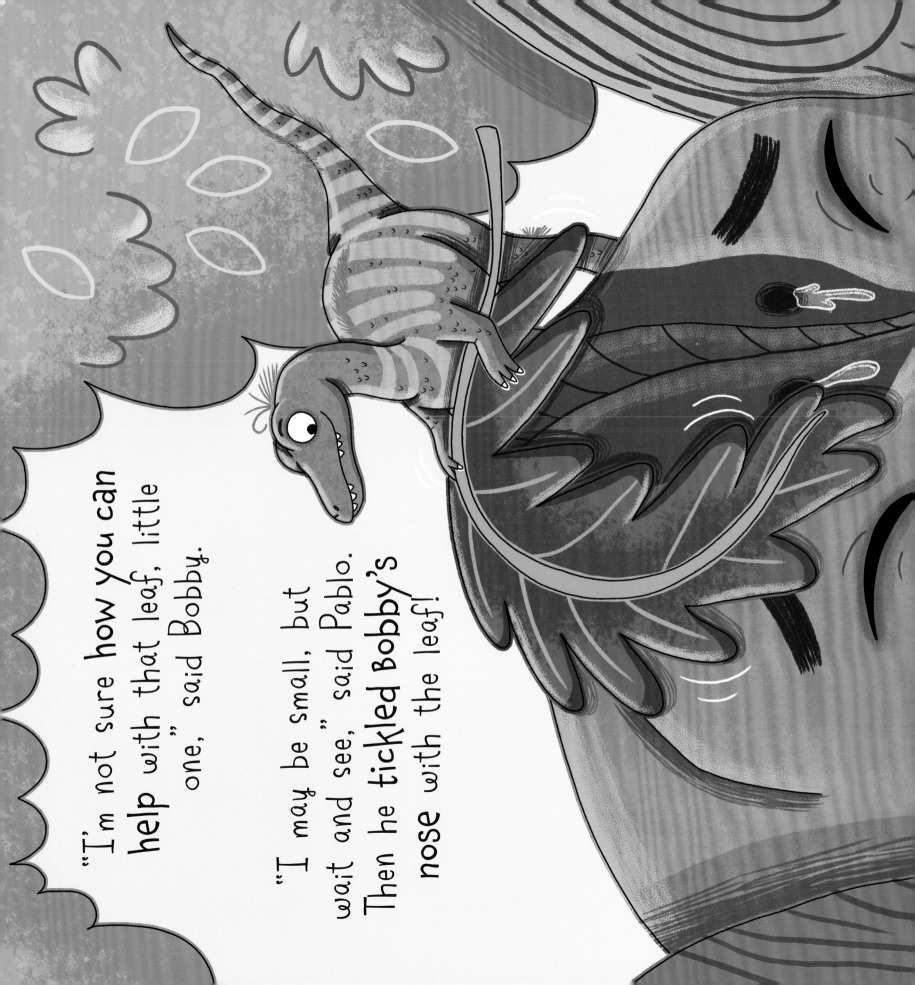

"I'm not sure how you can help with that leaf, little one," said Bobby.

"I may be small, but wait and see," said Pablo. Then he tickled Bobby's nose with the leaf!

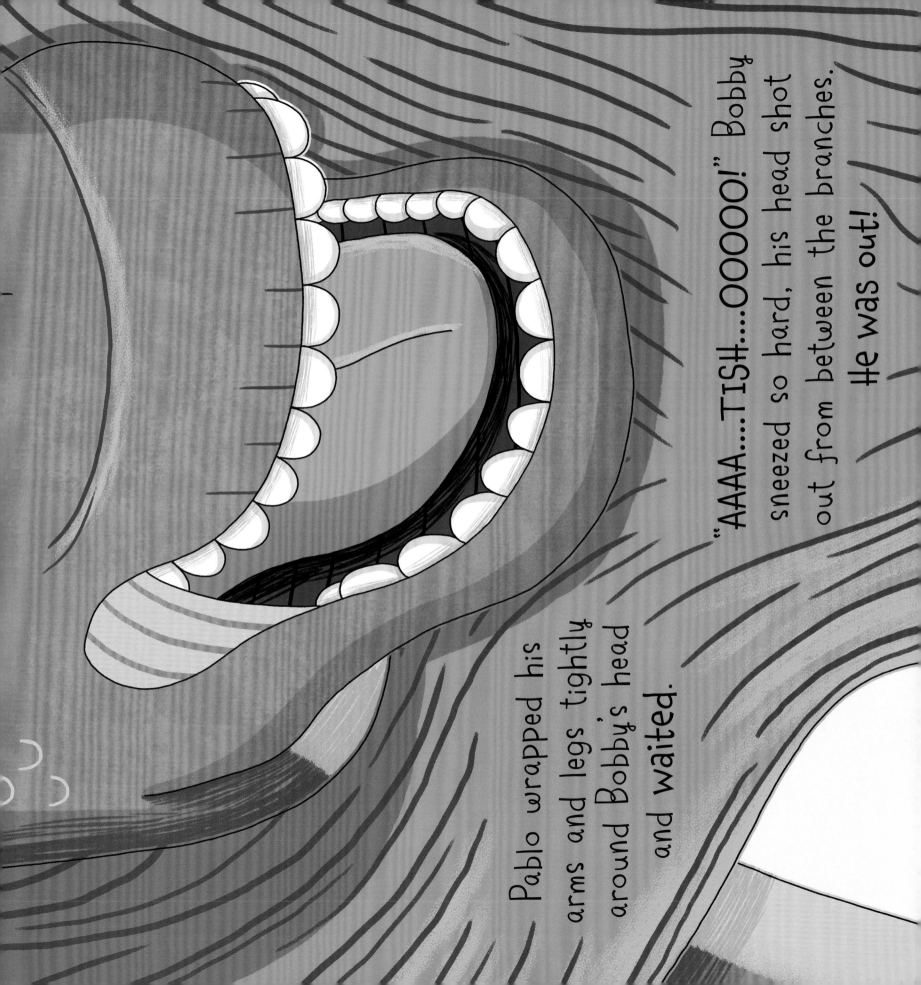

"AAAA...TISH...OOOOO!" Bobby sneezed so hard, his head shot out from between the branches. He was out!

Pablo wrapped his arms and legs tightly around Bobby's head and waited.

"It's good to be **curious**," said Ben as they escaped. "But always check before poking your nose into things!"

And the Megalosaurus was something Bobby did NOT want to find out about!